Tricking a dragon

Story written by Alison Hawes
Illustrated by Tim Archbold

Speed Sounds

Consonants   *Ask children to say the sounds.*

f	l	m	n	r	s	v	z	sh	th	ng
ff	ll	mm	nn	rr	ss	ve	zz			nk
ph	le	mb	kn	wr	se		se			
			gn		(c)		s			
					(ce)					

b	c	d	g	h	j	p	qu	t	w	x	y	ch
bb	k	dd	gg		g	pp		tt	wh			tch
	ck		gu		(ge)							
					(dge)							

Each box contains one sound but sometimes more than one grapheme.
*Focus graphemes for this story are **circled**.*

Vowels

Ask children to say the sounds in and out of order.

a	e ea	i	o	u	ay a͡-e a	ee ea y e	igh i͡-e ie i	ow o͡-e o oe
at	hen	in	on	up	day	see	high	blow

oo u͡-e ue	oo	ar	**or** **oor** **ore** **aw**	air are	ir ur er	ou ow	oy oi
zoo	look	car	for	fair	whirl	shout	boy

Story Green Words

Ask children to read the words first in Fred Talk and then say the word.

sore   trace   corn   fled   cheers*

Ask children to say the syllables and then read the whole word.

Zof|ia   Mar|ek   aw|ful   vill|age   a|side   e|ven   nev|er*

Ask children to read the root first and then the whole word with the suffix.

yawn → yawned   loud → loudly   force → forced

claw → claws   leave → leaving   gorge → gorged

brag → bragged   wait → waited*   strong → stronger*

* Challenge Words

Vocabulary Check

Discuss the meaning (as used in the story) after the children have read each word.

	definition:	**sentence:**
gorged	ate greedily	... the dragon gorged on their crops of corn and wheat.
crops	plants that farmers grow as food	... the dragon gorged on their crops of corn and wheat.
trace	draw	Marek and Zofia used a stick to trace a line on the forest floor.
flakes	thin pieces of something	... he saw the flakes fall to the ground.
bragged	showed off	"I can do that too!" bragged the dragon.
cast... aside	threw away	He cast the stone aside...
fled	ran away scared	... fled into the trees.

Red Words

Ask children to practise reading the words across the rows, down the columns and in and out of order clearly and quickly.

come	many	could	any
through	water	whole	watch
some	one	would	small
were	all	their	mother
how	old	people	should

Tricking a dragon

Marek and Zofia lived with their mother in a village on the edge of a dark forest. Deep in the forest lived a dragon. A dragon with awful claws and very big jaws.

Each night, the people watched from inside their homes as the dragon gorged on their crops of corn and wheat.

"Someone should stop that dragon," said Marek, "before it eats any more of our crops... or us!"

"Maybe we could do it..." said Zofia. "How could we get rid of a dragon with awful claws and very big jaws?" asked Marek. "All we need are some seeds and some grapes to trick him into leaving," said Zofia. She told Marek her plan.

The next evening, Marek and Zofia used a stick to trace a line on the forest floor. They waited for the dragon to arrive.

As the dragon came into sight, Marek shouted: "Stop!
You must not cross this line, or we will be forced to
fight you."

"Don't be so silly," snorted the dragon.
"I could crush you with one claw!"

"I may be small," said Marek,
"but I'm strong. I'll show you!"

"If you must," yawned the dragon.

"Look," Marek said, "I can crush this pebble into dust."
As he squeezed the pebble, he crushed the seeds hidden in his hand.
The dragon's jaw dropped as he saw the flakes fall to the ground.

"You might be strong," said the dragon, "but I am *huge*, so I would still win in a fight."

"I am even stronger than Marek," said Zofia. "I can squeeze this stone into water."

The dragon snorted very loudly.
"Don't be so silly!" he said. "You are far too weak to beat me!"

As Zofia squeezed the stone, she crushed the grapes hidden in her hand.
The dragon's jaw dropped as he saw the liquid drip on to the ground.

"Ha!" said Zofia. "So you see, Dragon, you may have awful claws and very big jaws, but I can squeeze water out of a stone!"

"I can do that too!" bragged the dragon.
"Show us, then!" said Zofia.

The dragon picked up a stone
and squeezed it.
He squeezed and squeezed until
his face was red and his claws
were sore... but still no water came out.

He cast the stone aside and fled into the trees.

Zofia smiled. "I said we could trick that dragon."
"And we did!" said Marek.

"Hurray! Three cheers for Zofia and Marek!" shouted the people. "Our village is safe."

"I don't think he'll come back," said Zofia... and he never did!

Questions to talk about

Ask children to TTYP each question using 'Fastest finger' (FF) or 'Have a think' (HaT).

p.9 (FF)   What did the people do when the dragon gorged on their crops?

p.10 (FF)   Zofia wanted to trick the dragon into leaving. What two things did she need?

p.11 (HaT) Marek said he would show the dragon how strong he was. Why did the dragon yawn?

p.12 (HaT) The dragon's jaw dropped when he saw the flakes. How do you think the dragon felt?

p.13 (HaT) Why did the dragon think Zofia was strong?

p.14 (HaT) Why did the dragon run away into the trees?

p.15 (HaT) Why did the villagers cheer for Zofia and Marek?

Questions to read and answer

(Children complete without your help.)

1. The dragon lived **on the edge of the village / deep in the forest / in a cave**.

2. Marek and Zofia traced **a shape / an animal / a line** on the forest floor.

3. "I may be small" said **Zofia / Marek / the dragon**, "but I'm strong..."

4. Marek crushed **the seeds / a stick / the pebble** in his hand.

5. The people in the village shouted **"Good morning" / "Hello" / "Hurray"** to Marek and Zofia.

Speedy Green Words

too	dark	stone	trees
homes	saw	more	inside
show	hand	next	eats
night	ground	deep	for
may	silly	floor	safe